G000252294

SNOOPY

features as

The Fearless Leader

Charles M. Schulz

ℛℛ

Copyright © 2001 United Feature Syndicate, Inc.
All rights reserved.
Licensed by PSL
(www.snoopy.com)

PEANUTS is a registered trademark of United Feature Syndicate, Inc.
Based on the PEANUTS® comic strip by Charles M. Schulz.

Originally published in 1988 as 'Snoopy Stars as the Fearless Leader'.
This edition published in the Year 2001 by Ravette Publishing.

This book is sold subject to the condition that
it shall not, by way of trade or otherwise, be
lent, resold, hired out or otherwise circulated
without the publisher's prior consent in any
form of binding or cover other than that in
which it is published and without a similar
condition including this condition being
imposed on the subsequent purchaser.

Printed and bound in Great Britain
for Ravette Publishing Limited,
Unit 3, Tristar Centre,
Star Road, Partridge Green,
West Sussex RH13 8RA
by Cox & Wyman, Berkshire

ISBN: 1 84161 104 2

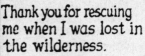

© 1979 United Feature Syndicate, Inc.

© 1979 United Feature Syndicate, Inc.

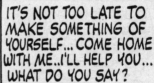

© 1979 United Feature Syndicate, Inc. 8-9

© 1980 United Feature Syndicate, Inc.

© 1985 United Feature Syndicate, Inc.

© 1980 United Feature Syndicate, Inc.

© 1981 United Feature Syndicate, Inc.

6 - 13

© 1983 United Feature Syndicate, Inc.

Other PEANUTS titles published by Ravette ...

Snoopy Pocket Books

Snoopy features as ...	ISBN	Price
Man's Best Friend	1 84161 066 6	£2.99
Master of the Fairways	1 84161 067 4	£2.99
The Fitness Fanatic	1 84161 029 1	£2.99
The Flying Ace	1 84161 027 5	£2.99
The Great Philosopher	1 84161 064 X	£2.99
The Legal Beagle	1 84161 065 8	£2.99
The Literary Ace	1 84161 026 7	£2.99
The Master Chef	1 84161 107 7	£2.99
The Matchmaker	1 84161 028 3	£2.99
The Music Lover	1 84161 106 9	£2.99
The Sportsman	1 84161 105 0	£2.99

Peanuts 'Little Book' series

Charlie Brown - Wisdom	1 84161 099 2	£2.50
Snoopy - Laughter	1 84161 100 X	£2.50
Lucy - Advice	1 84161 101 8	£2.50
Peppermint Patty - Blunders	1 84161 102 6	£2.50

Peanuts Anniversary Treasury	1 84161 021 6	£9.99
Peanuts Treasury	1 84161 043 7	£9.99

You Really Don't Look 50 Charlie Brown	1 84161 020 8	£7.99

Snoopy's Laughter and Learning series
wipe clean pages
(a fun series of story and activity books for preschool and infant school children)

Book 1 - Read With Snoopy	1 84161 016 X	£2.50
Book 2 - Write With Snoopy	1 84161 017 8	£2.50
Book 3 - Count With Snoopy	1 84161 018 6	£2.50
Book 4 - Colour With Snoopy	1 84161 019 4	£2.50

All PEANUTS™ books are available from your local bookshop or from the address below. Just tick the titles required and send the form with your payment to:-

BBCS, P.O. Box 941, Kingston upon Hull HU1 3YQ
24-hr telephone credit card line 01482 224626

Prices and availability are subject to change without prior notice.

Please enclose a cheque or postal order made payable to BBCS to the value of the cover price of the book and allow the following for postage and packing:-

UK & BFPO:	£1.95 (weight up to 1kg)		3-day delivery
	£2.95 (weight over 1kg up to 20kg)		3-day delivery
	£4.95 (weight up to 20kg)		next day delivery
EU & Eire:	Surface Mail:	£2.50 for first book & £1.50 for subsequent books	
	Airmail:	£4.00 for first book & £2.50 for subsequent books	
USA:	Surface Mail:	£4.50 for first book & £2.50 for subsequent books	
	Airmail:	£7.50 for first book & £3.50 for subsequent books	
Rest of the World:	Surface Mail:	£6.00 for first book & £3.50 for subsequent books	
	Airmail:	£10.00 for first book & £4.50 for subsequent books	

Name: ....

Address: ....

....

....

Cards accepted: Visa, Mastercard, Switch, Delta, American Express

Expiry date .... Signature ....